**Practice Book F**

# Thinking Skills

## Thinking in Content Areas

Consultant:  Barbara Z. Presseisen, Ed.D.
Authors:  Molly Rodgers & Linda Zimmer
Editor:  Christine A. Swanson
Design:  Nicole Eisenhauer

An Essential Learning Product ™

# Introduction for Parents and Teachers

Critical thinking skills are learned in early childhood and can be taught and practiced much like reading and writing. Essential Learning Products Thinking Skills provides a variety of mental exercises to set your child on a course of clear and logical thinking, the basis for success in school. Book F is intended for children in sixth grade. Children will be able to work independently or with adult guidance. Answers are provided at the end of the book. There are three clusters of skills in Book F.

## Naming, Matching, Sorting, Ordering

In this cluster the child learns to distinguish one item from another, to find likenesses and differences, to identify items by their qualities, and to sort them into categories. The child also arranges items and events in order by time, size, or pattern.

## Connecting, Predicting, Relating

This cluster of skills teaches the child to identify items that connect naturally or as part and whole. By predicting, the child decides what will happen next. By relating, the child finds the link between pairs of objects and makes the same link for other pairs.

## Concluding, Translating, Finding Causes

In the final cluster the child begins to acquire the skills of drawing conclusions when given a set of facts. Translating helps the child interpret the meaning of idiomatic expressions. By finding causes, the child grows to understand cause-and-effect relationships.

# Contents

# Student Introduction

Do you ever practice playing a musical instrument? Do you work on diving, dancing, or shooting baskets? Have you ever rehearsed a speech or a part in a play?

This book will help you practice thinking skills. You will practice finding things that are the same and things that are different, sorting things, and putting things in order. You will practice connecting things that go together, predicting what will happen next, and finding how things relate. You will practice drawing conclusions, interpreting expressions, and finding out what causes certain things to happen.

Many of these thinking skills you do already without even knowing it! Practicing thinking skills will help you make sense of things, make decisions about things, and find answers to problems.

Name the shapes you see in these figures.

1.

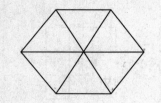

*triangle trapezium*

2.

*triangle square parallellogram*

3.

*star triangle polygon*

## Practice

Find the one on the right that is the same as the one on the left.
Circle the letter of your answer.

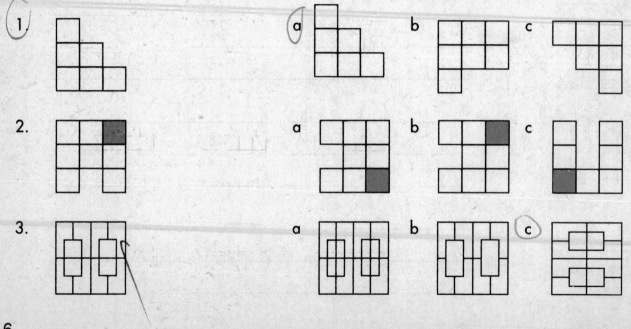

1.     a     b     c

2.     a     b     c

3.     a     b     c

Find the one on the right that is the same as the one on the left.
Circle the letter of your answer.

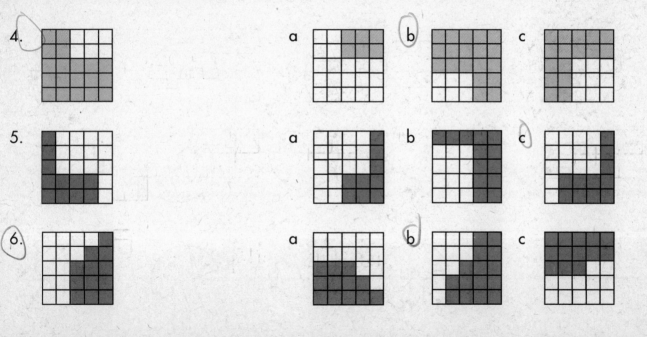

4.

a    b    c

5.

a    b    c

6.

a    b    c

# Practice

Which part should you join with **a** to make a circle?
Circle the letter of your answer.

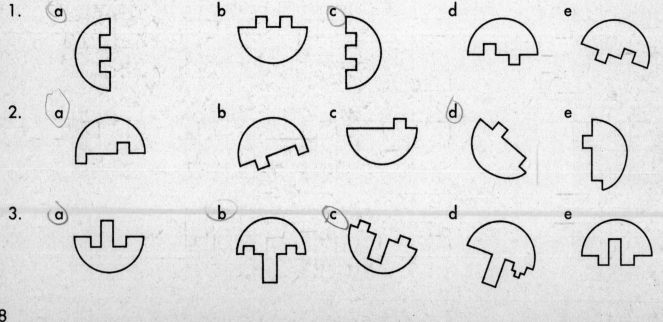

1. a    b    c    d    e

2. a    b    c    d    e

3. a    b    c    d    e

Which part should you join with **a** to make a square?
Circle the letter of your answer.

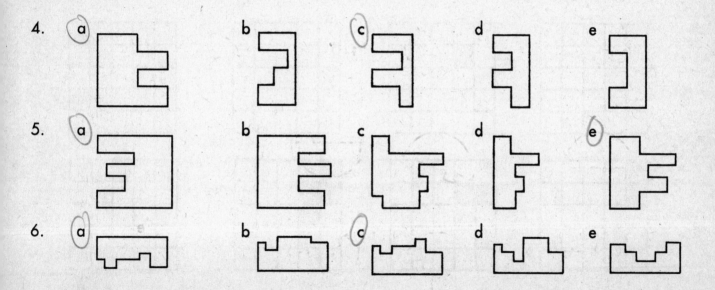

4. a   b   c   d   e

5. a   b   c   d   e

6. a   b   c   d   e

## Practice

Draw the one that comes next.

1.

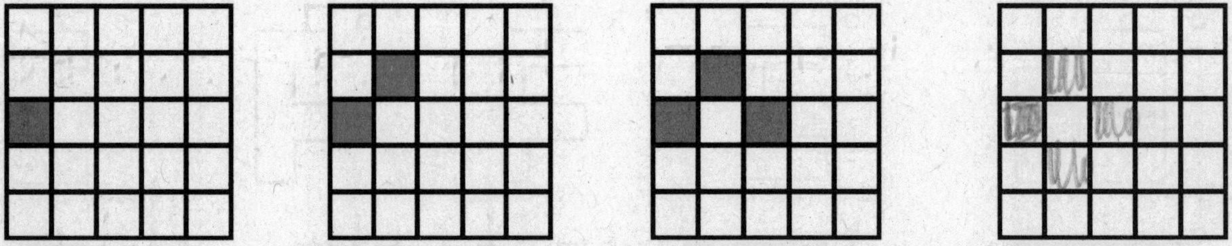

2.

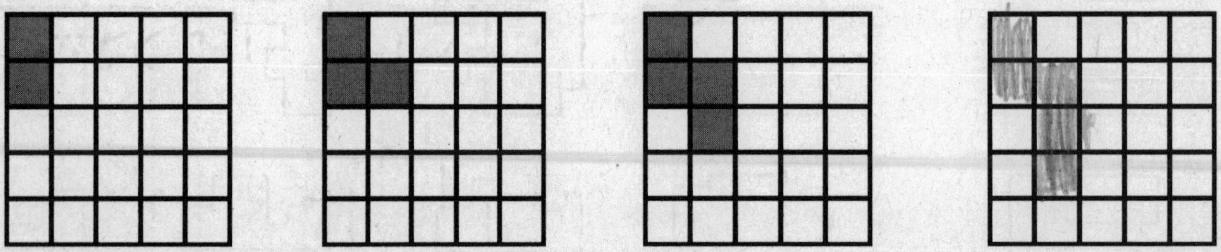

3.

4.

## Practice

In each group, cross out the word that does not belong. Then write why
it does not belong.

1. oak, maple, palm, ~~root~~, willow

Why? _because the root is not a tree._

2. cabin, mansion, church, cottage, ~~split-level~~

Why? _because its a tool._

3. velvet, ~~vest~~, wool, corduroy, denim

Why? _Its not a_

4. bear, cow, lizard, whale, giraffe

Why? _because its not a mammal_

5. island, cliff, peninsula, plateau, population

Why? _____

6. Iowa, Chicago, Georgia, Texas, Maine

Why? _____

## Practice

Each of these problems is impossible to solve because some information is missing. Read each problem. Write what is missing from the problem. One is done for you.

1. Mount McKinley is 20,320 feet high. Mount Blackburn is 2,413 feet higher than Pikes Peak. How much higher is Mount McKinley than Pikes Peak?

What is missing?     ___the height of Pikes Peak___

2. Mr. Carroll went grocery shopping. He spent $7.98 for chicken, $2.74 for cheese, $.79 for mustard, and $2.39 for bread. How much change did he receive?

What is missing? _____

3. Alex's family drove from their home to Florida for vacation. The first day they drove 340 miles. The second day they drove twice as far as the first day. The third day they drove 150 miles. How many miles do they still need to travel to reach Florida?

What is missing? _____

4. On one day at an amusement park, 714 people rode the ferris wheel, 2,147 rode the roller coaster, and 986 rode the carousel. If children's tickets cost $1.25 and adults' tickets cost $2.00, how much money was spent on the three rides?

What is missing? _____

## Practice

Read each problem. Write what you would do first to solve the problem. Remember that there can be more than one way to solve a problem.

1. Before you left school for the day, you checked your pocket, and your house key was there. You walked twelve blocks home. When you get to the door, there is no key in your pocket. The door is locked. What would you do first?

_____

_____

2. Your cousin lives far away in a place where it never snows. She wants to see and touch a real snowball. It snowed in your town last night. What would you do first?

_____

_____

3. Your parents allow you to start a garden in the backyard. The part of the yard that gets the most sun is very rocky. Another part has hardly any rocks, but it is shaded most of the day. What would you do first?

_____

_____


4. The power in your house went off just as you were about to cook a hamburger on the electric stove. A thunderstorm is starting outside. What would you do first?

_____

_____

# Practice

Complete the chart.

| | x4 | —— | —— | —— |
|---|---|---|---|---|
| 3 | 12 | 24 | 15 | 27 |
| 6 | —— | —— | —— | —— |
| 4 | —— | —— | —— | —— |
| 7 | —— | —— | —— | —— |
| 8 | —— | —— | —— | —— |

Complete the chart.

| | x7 | —— | —— | +12 |
|---|---|---|---|---|
| 9 | —— | —— | —— | —— |
| 12 | —— | 4 | —— | —— |
| —— | —— | 9 | —— | —— |
| 15 | —— | —— | 60 | —— |
| 56 | —— | —— | —— | —— |

19

## Practice

Each group of words is alike in some way. Write how they are alike. You may be able to find more than one way that they are alike.

1. stiffen, supper, stagger, slapped

_____

_____

2. nimbus, cirrus, cumulus, stratus

_____

_____

3. biking, jogging, wrestling, skiing

_____

_____

4. two, one, four, eight

_____

_____

5. slim, skinny, slender, scrawny

_____

_____

6. minute, wind, record, read

_____

_____

## Practice

Write how the figures are alike. Then write how they are different.

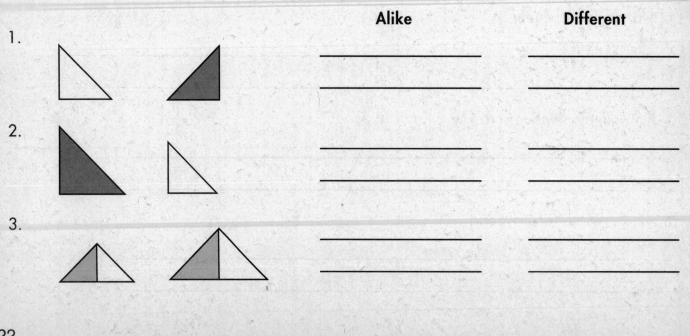

| | Alike | Different |
|---|---|---|
| 1. | _____ _____ | _____ _____ |
| 2. | _____ _____ | _____ _____ |
| 3. | _____ _____ | _____ _____ |

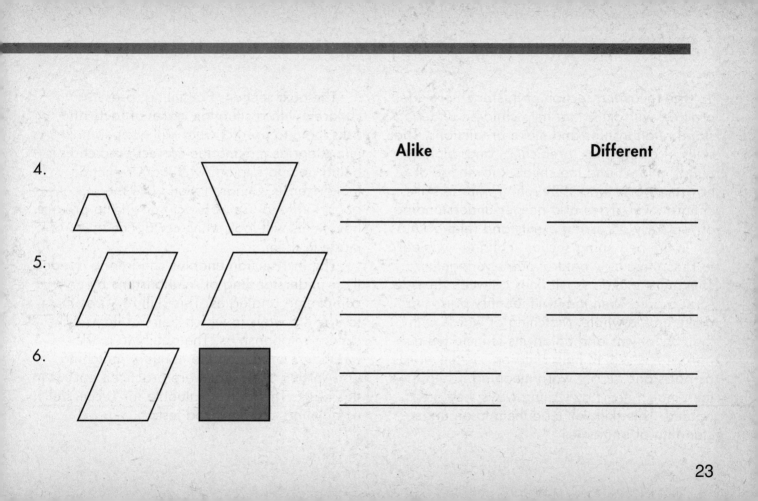

**Alike**

**Different**

4.

5.

6.

# Introduction to Connecting, Predicting, Relating

The following section of this book provides practice with skills that help children understand relationships and make predictions. The skills of connecting, predicting, and relating build on logic and the child's knowledge of how the world works. By refining these skills, children will arrive at a deeper understanding of regularly occurring events and relationships.

In the beginning section, children will learn to recognize how natural pairs go together. They must make associations between items to form a pair. Then they will identify parts that make up the whole. Matching of words with their synonyms and antonyms is included as part of this skill to help children see the words as pairs and clarify word meaning. Children then match items by writing ways they are related. This skill will lead them to an understanding of analogies.

The next section, Predicting, presents children with a situation or set of facts and asks them to predict what will happen next. As important as making the correct prediction is being able to explain why that prediction makes sense. Children then have the opportunity to use abstract thinking to predict how items will look when certain changes are made to them.

The last section enables children to deepen their understanding of relationships by completing analogies. This skill requires them to identify ways in which pairs of items have similar relationships. The ability to make analogies is built on the naming, matching, and sorting skills that were practiced earlier in this book. This skill is valuable for successfully completing standardized tests.

Match the pairs. Draw lines.

1. area   •       • a. cubic centimeters

2. volume   •       • b. degrees

3. perimeter  •       • c. pounds

4. weight   •       • d. square feet

5. angle   •       • e. meters

## Connecting

Match the pairs. Draw lines.

1. Asia          a. state

2. Oahu          b. country

3. Andes         c. continent

4. Tennessee     d. island

5. France        e. mountains

Match the pairs. Draw lines.

1. goalie

2. quarterback

3. shortstop

4. center

5. server

a. football

b. volleyball

c. basketball

d. hockey

e. baseball

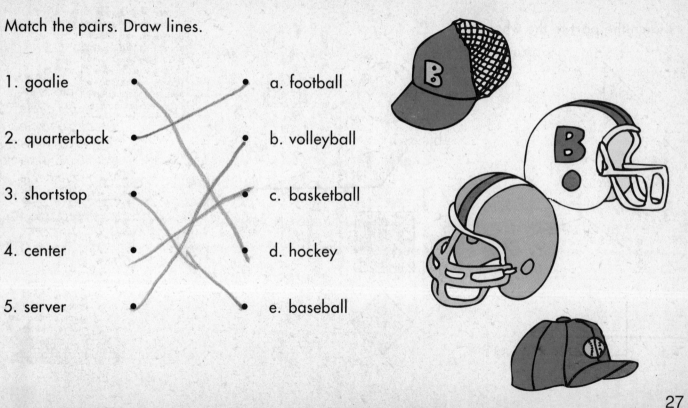

# Connecting

Match the part to the whole.

1.

2.

3.

4.

a.

b.

c.

d.

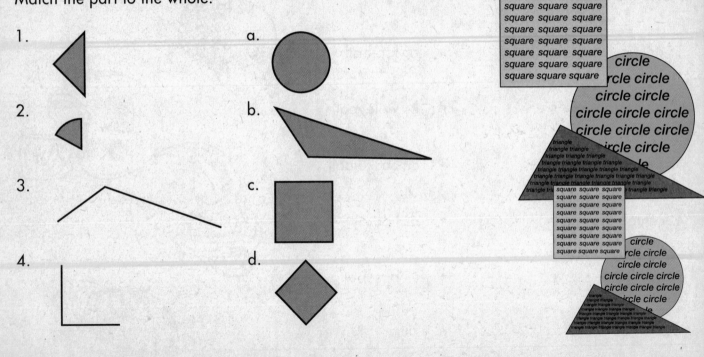

square square square
square square square
square square square
square square square
square square square
square square square
square square square
square square square
square square square

circle
circle circle
circle circle
circle circle circle
circle circle circle
circle circle

triangle
triangle triangle
triangle triangle triangle
triangle triangle triangle triangle
triangle triangle triangle triangle triangle
triangle triangle triangle triangle triangle triangle
triangle triangle triangle triangle triangle triangle
triangle triangle triangle triangle triangle triangle

square square square
square square square
square square square
square square square
square square square
square square square
square square square
square square square
square square square

circle
circle circle
circle circle
circle circle circle
circle circle circle
circle circle

triangle
triangle triangle
triangle triangle triangle
triangle triangle triangle triangle
triangle triangle triangle triangle triangle
triangle triangle triangle triangle triangle triangle
triangle triangle triangle triangle triangle triangle

28

Match the part to the whole.

1. nucleus

2. root

3. ventricle

4. star

5. atom

a. heart

b. plant

c. molecule

d. cell

e. constellation

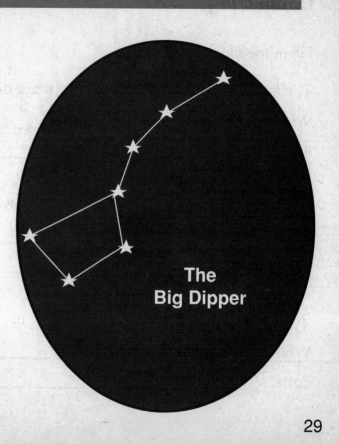

The
Big Dipper

## Connecting

Fill in the blanks.

1. character, dialogue, play, setting, stage directions

Whole: _____

Parts: _____   _____   _____   _____

2. monitor, printer, disk drive, computer, keyboard

Whole: _____

Parts: _____   _____   _____   _____

3. blood, circulatory system, arteries, veins, heart

Whole: _____

Parts: _____   _____   _____   _____

4. President, government, Senate, cabinet, Congress

Whole: _____

Parts: _____   _____   _____   _____

5. photograph, story, editorial, newspaper, advertisement

Whole: _____

Parts: _____   _____   _____   _____

6. barn, farm, fields, silo, pasture

Whole: _____

Parts: _____   _____   _____   _____

# Connecting

Write a word or phrase to tell how each pair of pictures is related.

**Example:** 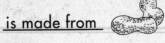 __is made from__ _____

1.  _____

2.  _____

3.  _____

4.  _____

Write a word or phrase to tell how each pair of words is related.

1. Brazil ____in____ South America

2. gasoline ____is____ fuel

3. starch ____make____ bread

4. lava ____in____ volcano

5. stanza ____is____ poem

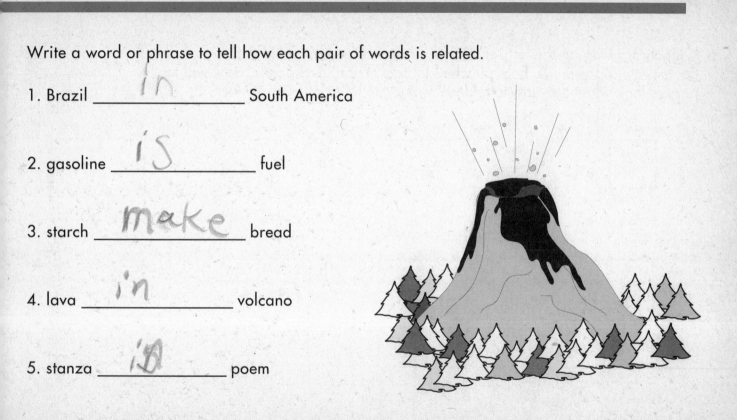

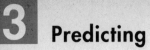

# Predicting

Each drawing on the left represents a piece of paper folded twice.
Each circle represents a hole punched through the folded paper. How will the papers look when they are unfolded? Circle the letter of your answer.

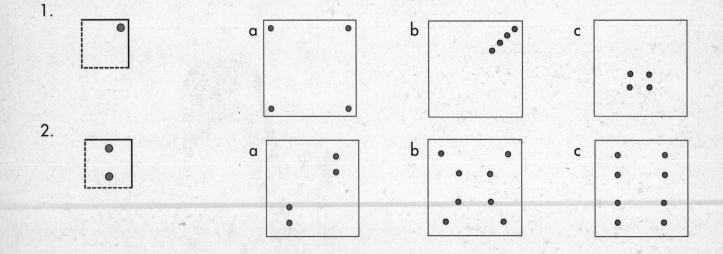

1.

a    b    c

2.

a    b    c

3.

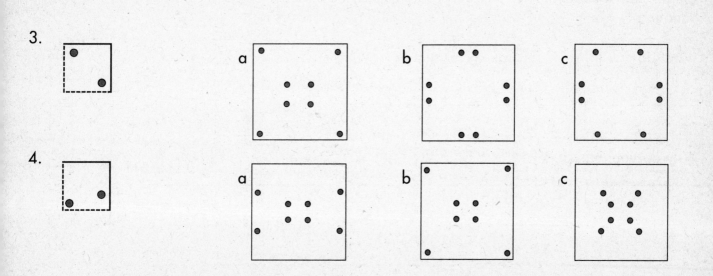

4.

## Predicting

Mrs. Jenkins is about to make dinner for her family. She takes a package from her kitchen cupboard. The package is marked: "This product is sold by weight, not volume. Some settling of contents may have occurred during handling."

What do you think she is making for dinner?

_____

Why do you think so?

_____

_____

_____

Mr. Jeffries painted his house two years ago. Some of the paint is peeling, and he wants to touch up the bare spots. He does not have any leftover paint.

What do you think he will do to get the same color of paint as he had before?

_____

Why do you think so?

_____


_____

# Predicting

Nina made a pizza for herself and five friends. She cut the pizza into six slices. Three more friends arrived just as the pizza was cut.

Write all the things you can think of that Nina might do next.

_____

_____

_____

_____

_____

Doug is doing a science project for school. He needs baking soda, but there is none in the house. The grocery store is closed. Doug's project is due tomorrow.

Write all the things you can think of that Doug might do next.

_____

_____

_____

_____

_____

_____

## Predicting

A store advertised a three-day sale on sneakers. The first day the store ran out of the sale sneakers. Customers continued to ask for the sneakers for the next two days.

Write as many things as you can think of that the store might do.

_____

_____

_____

_____

_____

_____

There have been two accidents at Jan's school this week. Both happened when students collided with each other while going up or down the stairs. The principal wants to prevent more accidents on the steps.

Write all the things you can think of that the principal might do.

_____

_____

_____

_____

_____

# 4 Relating

Circle the word that completes each phrase.

**Example:** strum : guitar :: beat : _____
     a. string     b. (drum)     c. song     d. stick
Read: "Strum is to guitar as beat is to ___drum___."

1. peel : banana :: shell : _____

     a. orange     b. beach     c. corn     d. egg

2. hawk : beak :: elephant : _____

     a. ear     b. trunk     c. claws     d. monkey

3. dentist : teeth :: forester : _____

     a. soil     b. animals     c. trees     d. rain

4. history : time :: geography : _____

     a. science     b. place     c. money     d. government

5. clue : hint :: take : _____
    a. remove       b. give       c. wish       d. idea

6. scientist : laboratory :: artist : _____
    a. canvas       b. paint       c. studio       d. brush

7. insult : flatter :: false : _____
    a. fake       b. cruel       c. imitation       d. sincere

8. over : numerator :: under : _____
    a. minuend       b. addend       c. fraction       d. denominator

9. shoe : leather :: sidewalk : _____
    a. cement       b. steel       c. street       d. traffic

## Relating

Circle the word that completes each phrase.

1. moist : humid :: dry : _____
    a. temperate    b. arid    c. polar    d. cool

2. story : author :: song : _____
    a. orchestra    b. music    c. composer    d. poet

3. smooth : silk :: rough : _____
    a. satin    b. velvet    c. cotton    d. burlap

4. boy : nephew :: girl : _____
    a. aunt    b. sister    c. uncle    d. niece

5. tree : maple :: nut : _____
    a. cashew    b. seed    c. shell    d. squirrel

6. attic : top :: _____ : bottom
   a. roof          b. yard          c. basement          d. steps

7. suitcase : clothing :: _____ : letter
   a. envelope      b. bag           c. stamp             d. pen

8. pear : fruit :: _____ : vegetable
   a. artichoke     b. lemon         c. garden            d. salad

9. nickel : five :: _____ : one
   a. dime          b. dollar        c. quarter           d. penny

10. forest : tree :: _____ : sand
    a. woods        b. desert        c. stone             d. canyon

# Relating

Circle the word that completes each phrase.

1. weight : kilograms :: _____ : degrees
   a. centigrade    b. temperature    c. thermometer    d. barometer

2. gray : black :: _____ : red
   a. blue    b. pink    c. orange    d. maroon

3. sorrowful : joyous :: _____ : smile
   a. scowl    b. sadly    c. laugh    d. cheer

4. advertisement : magazine :: _____ : television
   a. comedy    b. cartoon    c. commercial    d. videotape

5. equator : latitude :: _____ : longitude
   a. degree    b. North Pole    c. hemisphere    d. Prime Meridian

6. answer : question : _____ : problem
   a. discussion      b. solution      c. report      d. correct

7. numerous : many :: _____ : rise
   a. fall      b. up      c. remain      d. ascend

8. penny : dollar :: _____ : meter
   a. centimeter      a. millimeter      c. kilometer      d. decimeter

9. city : town :: _____ : box
   a. crate      b. lid      c. cardboard      d. bottle

10. driveway : house :: _____ : airport
    a. fence      b. plane      c. runway      d. luggage

# Relating

Circle the picture that completes each relationship.

1.

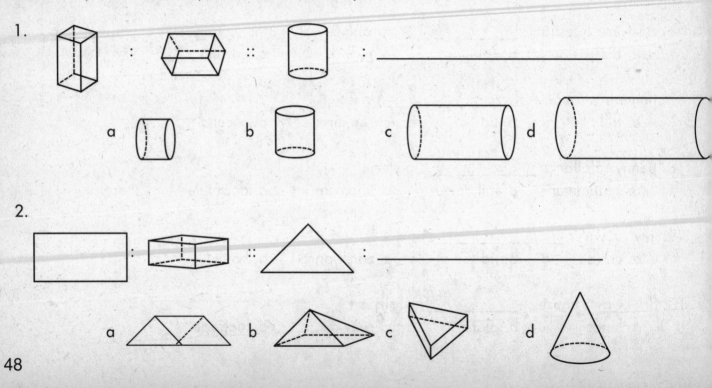

a     b     c     d

2.

a     b     c     d

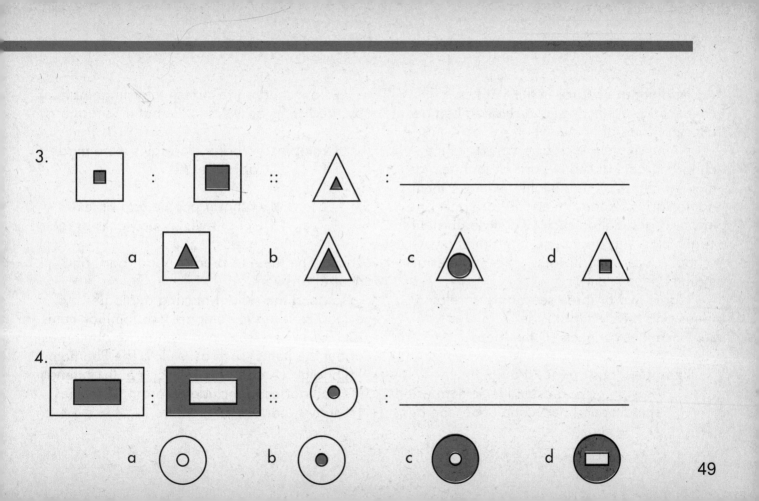

3.

a    b    c    d

4.

a    b    c    d

# Activities to Do at Home

Additional practice in the skills of connecting, predicting, and relating can be accomplished at home with these activities.

Name an item such as a car. Have the children name as many parts of that item as they can think of. You might also have them name various departments that are part of a larger organization such as a store (furniture, coats, clothing, appliances, perfume) or a school (classroom, library, office, cafeteria, maintenance room).

Name two or three seemingly unrelated ideas and have children use them in a sentence that connects all the ideas.

**Example:** bus, fudge, dramatic
Marian gave a dramatic scream when she dropped her fudge under the bus.

Allow children to stretch their imaginations by predicting answers to "What if" situations.

**Examples:** What if sidewalks were made of rubber?

What if people had an extra set of eyes in the backs of their heads?

Encourage them to predict good, bad, and neutral answers.

Extend the skill of making analogies by asking children to compare two familiar items, such as books. They can then make analogies about the items, such as: Milo : The Phantom Tollbooth :: Angie : Fly Like an Eagle. Extend the categories to include recordings, movies, TV shows, cartoon characters.

# Introduction to Concluding, Translating, Finding Causes

The final section of Thinking Skills Book F provides practice in skills that encourage children to interpret meanings and to establish cause and effect. The skills of concluding, translating, and finding causes require children to relate what is known to what is unknown and to relate outcomes to origins. Children build on the earlier thinking skills to move into more complex levels of thought.

First, children will practice drawing conclusions from information given. Activities include studying illustrations and reading short paragraphs for clues and then making inferences based on those clues. In most cases, there is no one right answer, but children should be encouraged to explain how they arrived at the conclusions they did.

Next, children will practice translating idioms. These are expressions which have special meaning beyond the literal sense of the words. Children will enjoy drawing pictures to illustrate the literal sense of the phrase, and then they will write interpretive sentences which will help them understand implied meanings and different ways of saying things.

Toward the end of the section, practice pages will focus children's attention on cause-and-effect relationships. Activities are built around analyzing outcomes and products to identify the reasons they happened. This skill will help children understand relationships between actions and outcomes. Encourage them to create their own games and activities using these skills.

# Concluding

To conclude is to decide something based on facts or information given. You have to think like a detective or a scientist. You look at the information you have and think about what it can tell you.

Read this sentence.

It was darker than any place Jay and Megan had ever been before, and the stone which surrounded them felt damp and cold.

What can you conclude about where Jay and Megan are?

The clues in the sentence are *darker than any place* and *damp, cold stone*. The first clue might indicate a room with no light or a cave. The second clue doesn't sound like a room though. Together, the clues reveal that Jay and Megan might be in a cave.

Imagine you are a detective and you find three pairs of clues in a room. Which item in each pair do you think provides more information about the criminal? Circle the item and explain your choice.

1. a road map   _____

   a compass   _____

   _____

2. sunglasses   _____

   eyeglasses   _____

   _____

3. a comb   _____

   a mirror   _____

   _____

# Concluding

What might you conclude if you overheard these partial conversations?

1. "I can't believe how hard that was. I think I did okay, but some of those questions were tough, and I really thought I studied everything last night!"

_____

_____

2. "She's so cute and so little! She likes to snuggle in my lap and have me scratch her behind her ears. Dad says she's going to grow fast though and won't fit in my lap for long."

_____

_____

3. "I'm going to have to take it in to the shop to get it fixed. I tried fiddling around with the chain but all I did was get grease on my fingers and jam the gear shift."

_____

_____

4. "Do you think he's figured out what's going on? I think we got everything ready without him catching us, but I'm afraid our excuse to get him here sounds suspicious."

_____

_____

5. "I really liked it. The special effects were amazing, and the casting was perfect. The only thing that bothered me was the noise from the people behind us."

_____

_____

# Concluding

Mr. Gabriel's class was doing a unit on health and nutrition. Students brought in four snacks. They compared the labels of column **a** to column **b** and column **c** to column **d**.

| **a** (raisins) | | **b** (salted cashews) | | **c** (ice cream) | | **d** (frozen yogurt) | |
|---|---|---|---|---|---|---|---|
| Per serving | | Per serving | | Per serving | | Per serving | |
| Calories | 250 | Calories | 170 | Calories | 120 | Calories | 80 |
| Protein | 3 g | Protein | 5 g | Protein | 2 g | Protein | 2 g |
| Carbohydrates | 66 g | Carbohydrates | 8 g | Carbohydrates | 18 g | Carbohydrates | 15 g |
| Fat | 0 g | Fat | 14 g | Fat | 5 g | Fat | 2 g |
| Sodium | 15 mg | Sodium | 135 mg | Sodium | 20 mg | Sodium | 4 mg |

**Healthy Eating**

In general, a healthy diet is composed of 20% protein (for growth and repair of body tissues), 50%-60% carbohydrates (for energy), 20%-30% fat (for energy and for certain vitamins). Sodium (salt) should total no more than 3,000 mg per day.

In the blank, write **a**, **b**, **c**, or **d** from the columns on page 56.

1. Which snack contains the most carbohydrates? _____

   The most fat? _____ The most protein? _____

   The most sodium? _____ The least amount of calories? _____

2. Would snacks from **a** or **b** be healthier? Explain.

   _____

   _____

3. Describe the differences between snacks from **c** and **d**.

   _____

   _____

# Concluding

Drawing accurate conclusions depends on the information you have and how you look at it. If your information is incomplete, or if you misinterpret or ignore clues, your conclusions may be faulty.

What is wrong with each of the following conclusions?

1. Allison's health assignment was to develop a low-salt menu plan for one week. She decided that things like bouillon cubes and soy sauce would be good for added flavor in recipes because she assumed they didn't have salt in them.

   _____

   _____

2. Daniel heard someone talking about tofu in class one day, so he bought some at the store later. He tried it at home, but it had so little taste to it, he concluded it had no nutritional value either.

   _____

   _____

3. Gloria went to a Japanese restaurant for the first time with her friend Liu. She watched the chef skillfully wrap up something she'd never seen before. These rolled bundles were beautiful to look at, and people seemed to enjoy them a lot. Liu explained that it was sushi—basically raw fish with rice or other ingredients. Gloria decided it must be awful.

_____

_____


4. Kareem's father had to go on a low-fat diet. While Kareem was grocery shopping, he found some prepared dinners that were labeled low-calorie. He bought several different kinds because he thought that anything low-calorie must also be low-fat.

_____

_____

# Concluding

In each of the following situations, is the conclusion accurate or faulty? If faulty, explain why, and write at least one other possible conclusion which could be reached.

1. During a football game, one team's star quarterback was injured. The team's back-up quarterback had not played in front of a crowd before, and the sportscaster concluded that the team wouldn't have a chance of winning now.

_____

_____

2. As Evelyn carried a jump rope outside, her grandfather commented on how boring jumping rope was. Evelyn invited him to watch her and her friends. He was amazed at the complicated steps and moves the four girls demonstrated, and he concluded that jumping rope could be a lot of fun.

_____

_____

3. There was a surprise contestant at the annual frog-jumping contest this year. It was a gigantic frog, bigger than anyone had ever seen before. Many onlookers in the stands concluded that because of its enormous size, it probably couldn't even get off the ground.

_____

_____


4. The rival high school basketball teams lined up on the court. The South School had one player who was a head taller than everyone else. The radio announcer concluded that the South School player was better than all the other players on both teams.

_____

_____

# Concluding

Sometimes a conclusion may be correct only temporarily. If you get additional information or if your information changes, you may need to revise your conclusion accordingly.

While running for election, Helen Kent ran only a few advertisements and rarely got in the news. Allen Hale had lots of ads with catchy slogans and had his picture taken with many groups and causes.

1. What do you think most people would conclude about who to vote for based on this information?

_____

In a debate, Ms. Kent responded intelligently to reporters' questions and displayed great understanding of the issues. Mr. Hale repeated his slogans and criticized Ms. Kent.

2. Would this information change people's decision about who to vote for? If so, how?

On election night, the first reports of the vote after the polls closed showed 75% for Hale and 25% for Kent.

3. What do you think people would conclude about the election based on this information?

_____

As more votes were counted and reported, the percentages began to change. Toward the end of the evening, Hale had 40% of the vote, and Kent had 60%.

4. Would this information change people's conclusions about the election? If so, how?

_____

_____

# Concluding

Sometimes clues can trick you! Be careful to analyze information carefully and keep an open mind.

1. Roberta and Louisa screamed. They slid from side to side as the car flew around the curves. Suddenly they were upside down, then right side up, and still speeding forward. They screamed again, but they weren't scared. Why not?

_____

_____

2. Leslie was telling her friends about her family's new pet. She'd named it Terry, and it was small with soft brownish-black fuzz. She brought it out cradled gently in her hands to show everyone, but no one would go near it. Why not?

_____

_____

3. Gary and Brent stood at the top of the mountain and surveyed the scene. The view was incredible from so high up. It seemed like it had taken them forever to reach the top, but now they knew it was worth it. They decided to stretch their legs and get some exercise before starting back down. They weren't even tired. Why not?

_____

_____

4. Francisco worked at a small nearby hospital. He liked talking to the patients, and they were usually happy to see him. Each afternoon, he went around making sure each one had fresh water. But he never had to change the sheets or get clean towels—the hospital didn't even have mattresses. Why not?

_____

_____

# Translating

To translate is to take a phrase or idea and express it in another form.

*Idioms* are phrases that have a distinct meaning greater than the words themselves, for example *(to be) a pain in the neck* or *(to be) in hot water*. To understand such phrases you have to go beyond the literal definition of the separate words and find a special meaning in the whole expression.

In this section you will practice translating phrases in two ways: first, you will be asked to draw a picture to illustrate the literal meaning of the expression; then, you will be asked to write a sentence describing perceived meaning, the way people actually interpret the expression.

**Example:**

Idiom: The food at that new restaurant is *out of this world*.

Translation: The food at that new restaurant is fantastic.

Choose one of these expressions. Draw a picture to illustrate its literal meaning. Then write a sentence to show its perceived meaning.

1. an idea that is off the wall
2. a person who is down to earth
3. an argument that is beside the point

_____

_____

# Translating

Choose one expression on each page. Circle the number of the one you choose. Draw a picture to illustrate the literal meaning of each expression. Then write a sentence to show its special meaning.

1. keep your head

2. catch my eye

3. stick her neck out                    4. play it by ear

_____

_____

# Translating

Choose one expression on each page. Circle the number of the one you choose. Draw a picture to illustrate the literal meaning of each expression. Then write a sentence to show its special meaning.

1. green with envy                    2. see red

_____

_____

3. tickled pink

4. out of the blue

_____

_____

# Translating

Choose one expression on each page. Circle the number of the one you choose. Draw a picture to illustrate the literal meaning of each expression. Then write a sentence to show its special meaning.

1. stretch a point                    2. pull yourself together

3. water it down          4. kick myself

# Translating

Read the paragraph below and underline the slang phrases and idioms. Then translate the paragraph so that it carries the same meaning but does not use slang or idioms. Rewrite the paragraph on page 75.

Two radio commentators were discussing city politics:

"Since the mayor got caught sleeping on the job, his political future seems to be hanging by a thread."

"Yes, and Jim Hughes has decided to take advantage of this mark on the mayor's record and take the plunge into the political waters."

"Last night I was at the meeting when Hughes announced he was throwing his hat into the ring. His announcement really fired up a lot people who have been on the mayor's case lately. They see Hughes as a knight in shining armor for the city."

"Hughes has said he wants to have a face-to-face with various city workers and kick around their solutions to the city's problems. Early reaction to his announcement would seem to indicate that he will walk away with the election."

# Translating

The meaning of certain words and phrases may change over time. Think of ways you use words such as **cool**, **hot**, and **bad**. Then ask parents, grandparents, or other adults how they use the same words. On this page, write examples of idioms using these idioms and others you use often. On page 77, translate the idioms into phrases. Avoid slang expressions in your translations.

1. _____
2. _____
3. _____
4. _____
5. _____
6. _____
7. _____
8. _____
9. _____
10. _____

1. _____

2. _____

3. _____

4. _____

5. _____

6. _____

7. _____

8. _____

9. _____

10. _____

# Finding Causes

To find causes is to identify the persons, things, or events that bring about outcomes or products.

When you think about causes of things, ask yourself questions.

**Example:** "What makes _____ happen?" (for example, "What makes water evaporate?");
"What makes a person _____?" (for example, "What makes the main character feel lonely?").

The answer is the cause. In the examples above, the cause is energy from the sun; losing a best friend.

Check the pairs in which the first object or event is a cause of the second.

____ 1. flower, spring      ____ 4. car exhaust, smog

____ 2. virus, illness      ____ 5. lack of rain, drought

____ 3. hammer, nail      ____ 6. tickling, laughter

What was the one cause of these inventions?

1.

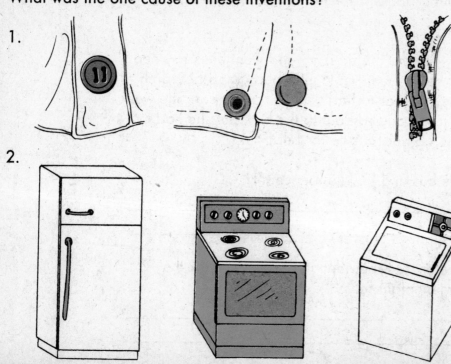

2.

# Finding Causes

Finding causes can help you understand problems that occur and how to avoid them.

Rebecca's alarm clock buzzed, but she turned it off and went back to sleep. Her mother came up and got her out of bed, but then Rebecca had to search through a pile of clean clothes on the floor to find something to wear. She went to the kitchen, gulped a glass of juice, and ran out to the bus, but she had forgotten her homework so had to go back inside for her books.

What caused Rebecca to miss the bus and be late for school?

_____

_____

Describe something that is a problem for you. Identify what you think the causes of the problem are and what might solve the problem.

_____

_____

You can also find causes in books and articles you read. In the Greek myth about Daedalus and Icarus, the thrill of flying causes Icarus to ignore his father's warnings and fly too close to the sun. Flying too close to the sun causes the wax to melt, the wings to fall apart, and Icarus to fall into the sea.

Select a book you have read and identify the causes of the conflict in the book and what causes the final outcome.

_____

_____

_____

_____

# Finding Causes

As you have seen, the events within a story can have a cause-and-effect relationship. There is also a cause-and-effect relationship between a story, such as in a book or movie, and the person who is reading or watching it.

Give an example of something in a book or movie that

1. caused you to laugh.

_____

_____

2. caused you to feel sad.

_____

_____

3. caused a feeling of suspense.

_____

_____

Imagine you are about to write a book or movie script. What kind of a story would you write? Humorous? Sad? Scary?

In the space below, briefly outline an idea you have for a book or movie. Describe the kind of effect you would want your book or movie to have on people and what events in your story might cause that effect.

_____

_____

_____

_____

_____

_____

# Finding Causes

A person's point of view and experience can influence what he or she sees as the causes of a particular situation. You may not agree with other people, but it is important to understand their points of view and why they identify different causes of the same outcome.

1. What might cause two brothers to argue over who is in charge when their parents are at work?

   From the older brother's point of view? _____

   _____

   From the younger brother's point of view? _____

   _____

2. What might cause a group of workers to go on strike?

From the workers' point of view? _____

_____

From the company's point of view? _____

_____

3. What might cause a person to approach a wild animal slowly and quietly?

From the person's point of view? _____

_____

From the animal's point of view? _____

_____

# Finding Causes

Several counties were suffering from low water levels in the reservoirs, and the city council was debating what to do about it. Local farmers said they needed water to irrigate their crops and grow needed food. City managers said they needed water to enable businesses to operate and homes to function.

What is the cause of the water shortage?

From the farmers' point of view? _____

_____

From the city managers' point of view? _____

_____

If you were a member of the city council, what would you suggest to resolve this problem?

_____

At summer camp Randy shared a bunk with a kid named Willy who had secretly brought his two pet snakes from home and hidden them under the bed. One night Randy woke up to feel something slithering all over him and he shrieked in surprise and fear. Everyone in the cabin woke up, but by the time the lights were on, the snakes had disappeared.

What is the cause of the problem?

From Willy's point of view? _____

_____

From the other campers' point of view? _____

_____

If you were the cabin counselor, what would you suggest to resolve this problem?

_____

# Finding Causes

Causes are sometimes part of a whole series of events. One event can cause a second event which can in turn cause a third event. These events can be part of a cycle or part of a progression which may continue into the future.

Discuss with a parent or a friend the following questions about causes and effects.

1. What causes animals to live in certain areas?

   a. What causes birds to migrate?
   b. What causes salmon to swim upstream?
   c. What causes prairie dogs to dig tunnels?

2. What can cause changes in an animal's habitat?

3. What can changes in habitat cause?

4. What can cause this chain of events to stop?

A single event may cause all sorts of different chains of events, both positive and negative.

Imagine a certain city has a problem with spreading out over the land. To protect certain natural areas nearby, it has proposed a law that all buildings must be at least 20 stories tall. What results might this law cause?

On page 90, list the positive outcomes in one column and the negative outcomes in another. When you have listed all the outcomes you can think of, compare your list with your friends' lists.

List all the different effects it might have on the city and its people—how they live, work, and play—and on the land, plants and animals.

# Finding Causes

| Positive Outcomes | Negative Outcomes |
|---|---|
| _____ | _____ |
| _____ | _____ |
| _____ | _____ |
| _____ | _____ |
| _____ | _____ |
| _____ | _____ |
| _____ | _____ |
| _____ | _____ |

Identify a problem you know of in your area.

_____

From your point of view, what caused this problem?

_____

_____

From other people's points of view, what caused this?

_____

_____

In your opinion, what would cause this problem to be solved?

_____

_____

# Finding Causes

Think about your solution to the problem on page 91. Make a list of all the possible other outcomes or effects your solution could have.

| Positive Effects | Negative Effects |
|---|---|
| _____ | _____ |
| _____ | _____ |
| _____ | _____ |
| _____ | _____ |
| _____ | _____ |
| _____ | _____ |

Are there more positive or more negative effects? Do you still think your solution is a good one?

# Activities to Do at Home

Conversations with children will offer many chances to focus and apply the skills practiced in this last section.

Children often jump to conclusions about who did something, about who will do something, about what others think. When this happens, ask them to explain what their conclusions are based on. Do not concentrate on the conclusion itself but on the strength of the evidence and the reasoning the child uses. Help children recognize when the conclusion is legitimate and when it is illogical. You might also play various guessing games like "Clue" or "Mastermind" which ask players to draw conclusions in order to win.

Listen for idioms people use in conversation. Idioms are often characteristic of a certain age or generation, so that the phrases a grandparent uses may not be clear to a child and vice versa. Idioms are also difficult for those who speak English as a second language. When children hear someone use an idiom, discuss its literal sense and its implied meaning, what it "really" means, and then how the listener perceives the words.

To work on cause and effect, you might watch the evening news with your children. Discuss specific events and the causes behind these events. Encourage them to recognize that a problem may have a number of related causes and that different points of view influence the ways people define the cause of a problem. Understanding cause-and-effect relationships helps to foster better communication skills. It helps us to clarify our ideas, too.

# Answers

## Page 5
1. triangles, diamonds, hexagon
2. triangles, square, parallelogram
3. triangles, pentagon, star

## Page 6, 7
| | | |
|---|---|---|
| 1. c | 2. a | 3. c |
| 4. b | 5. c | 6. a |

## Page 8, 9
| | | |
|---|---|---|
| 1. b | 2. e | 3. e |
| 4. c | 5. e | 6. c |

## Page 10, 11
1.    2.
3.    4.

## Page 12, 13
1. root—does not name a kind of tree
2. church—does not name a style of house
3. vest—does not name a kind of fabric
4. lizard—does not name a mammal
5. population—does not name a land form
6. Chicago—does not name a state

## Page 14, 15
2. the amount of money Mr. Carroll gave the cashier
3. the distance from Alex's home to Florida
4. the number of adults and children who rode each ride

## Page 16, 17 *
1. Check other pockets for key.
2. Make a snowball and put it in the freezer.
3. Find out about plants that grow well in shade.
4. Put the hamburger into the refrigerator.

## Page 18
| | x4 | x8 | x5 | x9 |
|---|---|---|---|---|
| 3 | 12 | 24 | 15 | 27 |
| 6 | 24 | 48 | 30 | 54 |
| 4 | 16 | 32 | 20 | 36 |
| 7 | 28 | 56 | 35 | 63 |
| 8 | 32 | 64 | 40 | 72 |

## Page 19
| | x7 | +3 | x4 | +12 |
|---|---|---|---|---|
| 9 | 63 | 3 | 36 | 21 |
| 12 | 84 | 4 | 48 | 24 |
| 27 | 189 | 9 | 108 | 39 |
| 15 | 105 | 5 | 60 | 27 |
| 56 | 392 | 18.66 | 224 | 68 |

## Page 20, 21 *
1. All words begin with s, have a short vowel sound, have a double consonant in the middle, and have e as the next-to-last etter.
2. All words name kinds of clouds and end with s.
3. All words name kinds of sports that do not use a ball. All words end in ing.
4. All words name numbers. All words have homophones (to/too, won, for, ate).
5. All words begin with s and are synonyms for thin.
6. All words have more than one correct pronunciation.

## Page 22, 23
1. Alike: shape, size. Different: color, direction.
2. Alike: shape, direction. Different: size, color.
3. Alike: shape, divided in half. Different: size, location of shading.
4. Alike: shape, color. Different: size direction
5. Alike: shape, color. Different: proportion.
6. Alike: four sides, parallelograms. Different: angles, color

* Answers may vary. Possible response is provided.

**Page 25**
1. d     2. a     3. e     4. c     5. b

**Page 26**
1. c     2. d     3. e     4. a     5. b

**Page 27**
1. d     2. a     3. e     4. c     5. b

**Page 28**
1. d     2. a     3. b     4. c

**Page 29**
1. d     2. b     3. a     4. e     5. c

**Page 30**
1. Whole: play   Parts: character, dialogue, setting, stage directions
2. Whole: computer   Parts: monitor, printer, disk drive, keyboard
3. Whole: circulatory system   Parts: blood, arteries, veins, heart
4. Whole: government   Parts: President, Senate, cabinet, Congress
5. Whole: newspaper   Parts: photograph, story, editorial, advertisement
6. Whole: farm   Parts: barn, fields, silo, pasture

**Page 32**
1. dries   2. cleans   3. runs on
4. is made from

**Page 33**
1. is part of   2. is a kind of   3. is contained in
4. comes from   5. is part of

**Page 34, 35**
1. a     2. c     3. b     4. a

**Page 36 ***
macaroni and cheese, spaghetti. Boxes for these products are marked as described.

**Page 37 ***
He might take a paint chip to the store to match, or borrow paint charts from the store and match with the house. He needs to match the paints from the store to the paint on the house.

**Page 38 ***
Nina might cut each of the six slices in half to have twelve slices; she might bake another pizza; she might offer the three new friends something different; she might order a pizza to be delivered.

**Page 39 ***
Doug might borrow some baking soda from a neighbor; he might look for another project that doesn't require baking soda; he might ask the teacher if he can turn in his project late; he might find a store that is open all night.

**Page 40 ***
The store might offer the customers rain checks; it might offer the customers sneakers of equal value; it might put a sign on the door that the sneakers were sold out; it might send customers to a different store that has the sneakers.

**Page 41 ***
The principal might assign students to monitor the stairways; she might set aside one stairway for going up only and one for going down only; she might direct the students to walk on one side when going up and the other side when going down.

**Page 42, 43**
1. d     2. b     3. c     4. b
5. a     6. c     7. d     8. d     9. a

**Page 44, 45**
1. b     2. c     3. d     4. d     5. a
6. c     7. a     8. a     9. d     10. b

**Page 46, 47**
1. b     2. d     3. a     4. c     5. d
6. b     7. d     8. a     9. a     10. c

**Page 48, 49**
1. d     2. b     3. b     4. c

**Page 53 ***
1. The road map gives a clue about where the criminal may be heading.
2. The eyeglasses gives a clue about whether the criminal is nearsighted or farsighted and possibly whether male or female depending on style of glasses.
3. The comb might have a strand of hair in it which would give a clue about the length and color of the criminal's hair.

**Page 54, 55**
1. The person speaking just took a test.
2. The person speaking just got a new puppy.
3. The person speaking has a broken bicycle.
4. Some people are having a surprise party for someone.
5. The person speaking just saw a movie or play.

---

* Answers may vary. Possible response is provided.

95

**Page 57**
1. a, b, b, b, d
2. a is healthier because it is lower in fat and sodium.
3. d is healthier because it is lower in fat, sodium, and calories.

**Page 58, 59**
1. Allison did not look for label information on salt content; she ignored clues and jumped to a conclusion.
2. Daniel misinterpreted clues, because taste is not the same as nutritional value.
3. Gloria ignored the positive clues she saw at first and based a conclusion on incomplete information since she did not taste it.
4. Kareem misinterpreted clues, because something can be low-calorie but still have a lot of fat in it.

**Page 60, 61 ***
1. The conclusion is faulty because no one knew how the back-up quarterback would play; the sportscaster might conclude that everyone will just have to watch to find out who wins.
2. The conclusion is accurate.
3. The conclusion is faulty because size is not the only factor that influences ability to jump. Onlookers might conclude that the frog could jump farther because its legs were bigger.
4. The conclusion is faulty because being taller does not necessarily make someone better. The announcer might conclude that the player's height might give him an advantage at times, but that other players might have more speed or accuracy.

**Page 62, 63 ***
1. Most people would vote for Hale because he had greater visibility.
2. Yes; Kent's ability would convince people to vote for her.
3. Most people would conclude that Hale would win.
4. Yes; people would conclude that Kent would win.

**Page 64, 65 ***
1. They were on a roller coaster.
2. Her new pet was a tarantula.
3. They had ridden to the top in a car or a ski-lift chair.
4. It was an animal hospital.

**Page 67 ***
Answers should suggest an idea that is bizarre or unreasonable; a person who is practical or realistic; an argument that does not apply.

**Page 68, 69 ***
Answers should suggest keeping (one's) self-control, staying calm; getting (one's) attention; taking a chance, risking failure or teasing; to improvise, to play music without seeing the notes, or to proceed without a plan.

**Page 70, 71 ***
Answers should suggest being envious; being angry; being happy or pleased; coming without notice or warning.

**Page 72, 73 ***
Answers should suggest making an exception, exaggerating; regaining control of oneself; weakening or diluting something; blaming oneself.

**Page 74, 75**
"Since the mayor got caught ignoring his responsibilities, his political future seems to be uncertain.

"Yes, and Jim Hughes has decided to take advantage of the mayor's failing and start working in the area of politics."

"Last night I was at the meeting when Hughes announced he was entering the election contest. His announcement really excited a lot of people who have been criticizing the mayor lately. They see Hughes as a champion of the city."

"Hughes has said he wants to meet with various city workers and informally discuss their solutions to the city's problems. Early reaction to his announcement would seem to indicate that he will easily win the election."

**Page 78**
Numbers 2, 4, 5, and 6 should be checked.

**Page 79**
1. the need to fasten parts of clothing together
2. the need to function more efficiently and reliably (than a coal or wood stove, an icebox, a wringer machine or washboard)

---

* Answers may vary. Possible response is provided.

96